# THE HARE AND THE TORTOISE

*To Dirk Jan*

# The Hare and

# the Tortoise

pictures by Paul Galdone

McGRAW-HILL BOOK COMPANY
New York • Toronto • London • Sydney

THE HARE AND THE TORTOISE is one of the most famous of AESOP's fables. Very little is known of AESOP except that he was born about 620 B.C. and died about 564 B.C. He was a Greek slave of Samos whose master set him free.

he Hare once boasted of his speed
before the other animals.

"I have never yet been beaten," said he, "when I put forth my full speed."

"I challenge any one here
to race with me."

The Tortoise said quietly,
"I accept your challenge."

"That's a good joke," said the Hare.
"I could dance around you
all the way."

"Keep your boasting
till you've beaten,"
answered the Tortoise.
"I accept your challenge."

So a course was fixed,

and a start was made.

The Hare darted almost out of sight at once,
but

soon stopped, and
to show his contempt
for the Tortoise,

lay down to have a nap.

The Tortoise
plodded on and

plodded on, and

when the Hare awoke
from his nap, he saw
the Tortoise just near
the winning post and

could not run up in time
to save the race.

Then said the Tortoise,

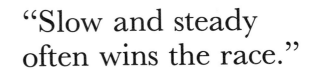

"Slow and steady
often wins the race."